THE FIELD GUIDE TO GNOMES

The Field Guide to Gnomes
First published in Great Britain in 2014
Armcher Productions Ltd.
www.armcher.com

ISBN 978-1-905672-39-4
Copyright © Armand Foster 2014

Printed and bound in China by C&C Offset Printing Co. Ltd.

This book is for my lovely
and incredibly
patient wife, Cheryl
who thought she
was marrying
a sane man.

With love.

4

CONTENTS

INTRODUCTION

I was brought up in Kenya in East Africa where my passion for wildlife was deeply instilled in me. I was a dedicated amateur naturalist and I also painted the natural world with some financial success.

Some thirty years ago I moved to the United Kingdom and discovered with great pleasure that Britain had varied and interesting flora and fauna.

To be as close to nature as possible, my wife and I bought an abandoned farm in the West of Wales. The farm, some forty acres in extent, was on the side of a valley below the highest point in the South West of Wales and comprised of rough pasture, woods and a beautiful river tumbling down the valley. There were upland peat bogs, scrub land, and ancient oaks - truly a naturalist's paradise. The farm had been abandoned in the great depression of the 1930's and had lain undisturbed for 60 or more years. We discovered that the wildlife, having been undisturbed for so long, was amazingly tame and unworried by our presence. Amongst the prolific wildlife there was a large population of badgers. These animals fascinated me and I spent many hours watching them. One morning, just after dawn, I was silently watching a hole under a bank that I thought might be part of a badger sett.

I had been completely motionless for about an hour when I noticed a movement in the hole.

To say I was amazed would have been an understatement, because a small face appeared, soon after followed by a second.

I was looking at a pair of Gnomes.

I resolved there and then to find out as much as I could about Gnomes. That was more than twenty years ago. My wife and I never realised at the time that this research would take us to the far corners of the planet and to every nook and cranny on the island of Britain. It has been a fascinating journey resulting in this book, the Field Guide to Gnomes.

Our old farm in *West Wales* was the perfect starting point. It was here that I started to study our local Gnomes, but more importantly the Gnomes got to know me, and once they realised that I was harmless, became positively enthusiastic in their efforts to help my research.

PROFESSOR DOKTOR DNAMRA RETSOF

It was during the early 1990's that I was contacted by the world's greatest Gnome expert, Herr Professor Doktor Dnamra Retsof, Director of the Institute of Gnomology in Munchen Gnomebach.

GNOME GENETICS

Professor Retsof is the man who single handedly (he lost the other one in a fight with a polar bear), deciphered the Gnomes' Genetic Code or G-Gnome. His sphere of research is vast but in brief he has discovered that, instead of having the DNA (Deoxyribonucleic acid) in a double helix pattern like we human beings, the Gnomes' DNA is a TRIPLE helix.

This results in the Gnomes having such incredibly robust health that they are immune to virtually all the diseases known to man.

Professor Retsof hopes that in time he will find ways of transferring this incredible immunity to humans.

This genetic makeup gives the Gnomes another advantage - their extreme longevity. Professor Retsof estimates that we live on average seven years to the Gnomes' one. Interestingly though, the Gnomes still work on the same years as do we humans, based on the sun. The main difference is that a Gnome year runs from the Summer Solstice on the 21st of June which is the Gnome New Year.

So a Gnome will easily live for some four hundred years, enjoying excellent health for his full life span.

Gnomes do however die in accidents, rarely their fault but sadly often at the hands of we humans. Motor vehicles are the main cause of Gnome mortality, but also increasingly too, from accidents with farm equipment.

Having cracked the Gnomes G-Gnome, Professor Retsof has undertaken extensive research into the origin of Gnomes.

Human beings share some 99% of their genes with the chimpanzee (Pan troglodytes) who come from the forests of Central Africa. This gave Professor Retsof a clue as to where to start.

II

The Professor spent years searching the forests of East and Central Africa. He even researched the lemurs of Madagascar. At the turn of the century I joined the Professor on a trip to Kenya, my old home. It was whilst sitting around a campfire one night that the Professor asked me what was making the eerie wailing sound we could hear. I casually replied 'a bushbaby'.

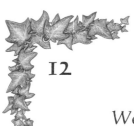

We both sat listening to the cry which was far louder than the myriad other sounds of the African night. Suddenly the Professor leapt to his feet. Maybe, just maybe, we had our answer! We then began a long search for bushbabies, and the even more difficult task of obtaining samples from them.   Eventually a friend from the Wildlife Department told me of a rare and seldom seen bushbaby that lived in the forests of Mount Kenya.   Not only did he know where they were, but had a friend who had a young bushbaby that had been rescued in the forest.   DNA tests on the Mount Kenya Bushbaby (Otolemur gnomettii) revealed that it was the closest ancestor to Gnomes with a DNA that was 99.97% the same as Gnomes.   However, extensive research has failed to find any Gnomes in that part of Africa. Professor Retsof's theory for this is that the Gnomes have been heavily hunted by hyenas, who have a great appetite for bushbabies and this, together with bilharzia (a waterborne disease prevalent in that part of the world that Gnomes have no resistance to), has decimated the Gnome population.

THE ART OF TRACKING GNOMES

Gnomes in 'the wild' are incredibly difficult to see. They are by nature shy and tend to move only when they are sure that no humans are in the vicinity.

Gnomes, however, like all animals, leave tracks when they move about their territories. To find them you must be able to 'read' the signs.

I was taught to track when very young by highly skilled African hunters and believe it or not, tracking is an art anyone can master. The first point you have to understand is that your eyes are like cameras, they record everything that is there, exactly as it is. The problem is the brain, which has been conditioned to see what it wants to. With practise you can see what is there and once you master the art, tracking will become second nature. When I walk in the wild, my eyes constantly scan the ground. It's like reading a newspaper of who has been around in the animal world and what they've been doing. Look for patches of mud or fine powdered dry ground - you will soon start to see and recognise the tracks and signs. Here are some of the more common tracks you will encounter:

On the right you have the spoor of a badger, almost bear like in their appearance. While below, on the left, are the pug marks made by a cat.

Top of the page on the right, are the tracks left by a fox.

Below and right of the fox are the footprints of a mouse. Note also with a mouse, there are usually drag marks left by the mouse's tail.

On the right below the mouse you have a rabbit's spoor. Please note these are not to scale, and also spoor size will vary with the size and age of the animal. Note how the rabbit's hind paws leave a long narrow imprint.

The final spoor on this page is that of an otter. The point to notice with this spoor is the obviously webbed toes, a sure sign the marks are made by an otter.

The top right hand spoor on this page is the spoor of a polecat. This spoor is very similar to that left by both weasels and stoats, the main difference being size.

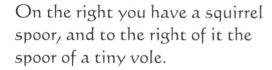

Below the polecat you have the imprint of a weasel, smaller than the polecat with several identifiable differences.

On the right you have a squirrel spoor, and to the right of it the spoor of a tiny vole.

Finally on this page you have the two spoor of deer, Roe Deer on the left and Red Deer on the right. In both instances the hoof print on the right is an imprint in soft mud, where the heavier animal tends to sink, so its spoor splays or, in the case of the Roe, slips slightly.

I have left the Gnome tracks till last, after the deer, as these are the spoor they are most often confused with.

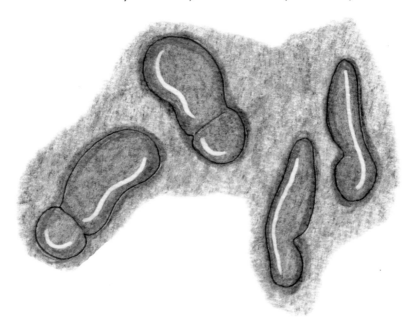

There are two sets of tracks in the illustration. The spoor on the left is a Gnome walking normally. The difference between this and the deer spoor is the markedly pigeon toed gait of the Gnomes. Every Gnome I have ever encountered walks with his toes pointing inward. Gnomes however are well aware that they leave tracks so that in areas where they risk being seen, they employ 'anti-tracking' tactics. The favourite device is to walk on the sides of their feet, their soft supple boots making this possible. The tracks left then are usually ignored as being the marks of a Roe deer. When they do not want to be noticed at all, a Gnome at the rear of a group will often walk backwards re-arranging disturbed vegetation and covering up marks in the mud or dust. Using these techniques they become virtually invisible.

One certain method to establish whether or not you have Gnomes in the area is the dock leaf test.

Gnomes use squares of dock (Rumex obtusifolius) leaves as toilet paper, so always look for dock leaves in the woods or in hedgerows and examine them carefully for the small square holes cut out of the leaves by Gnomes.

Gnomes also use dock leaves as a wrapping to keep Gnome butter (a delicious spread made from the fat obtained from hazel nuts).

The chemicals in the leaves keep both the butter and the Gnomes' backsides fresh.

DOCK Rumex obtusifolius

THE GNOME

THE GNOME

The Male Gnome height varies from 8 to 12 inches, (20 to 30 cm's)

Red hat or 'HATTON'. With one or two exceptions always red. Stiff and pointed when new but becomes soft and floppy with age.

Beard long and grey and nearly always a full beard or 'set', rarely if ever trimmed.

Shirts and trousers coarse woven woollen fabric, always muted colours to aid concealment.

Suede jerkin held closed by leather belt at waist with large brass polished buckle.

Always has a belt pouch for essentials and more often than not carries a beautifully crafted tool, usually a knife or axe.

Nearly always seen with a snake stick - a forked stick - to keep over amorous snakes at bay.

Suede boots are the norm but Gnomes are often also seen in waterproof 'Wellies'.

THE GNOME

The female Gnome or GNOMETTE, height similar to male.

Always seen wearing the red hat or HATTON.

Females do not have any facial hair and their hair is either long in plats or curled as in this example.   The curled hair usually denotes a married Gnomette.

The clothes are identical to the male Gnomes, but they are more likely to carry a small hand axe rather than a knife.

Gnomes and Gnomettes do not differentiate with tasks, both carry out identical tasks when the need arises.

A single large ear ring is worn as the only jewellery. Buttons and buckles, as with the males, are always highly polished brass.

Gnomettes have smooth unblemished, wrinkle free skin that never changes during their lives.

THE GNOME
IMMATURE OR JUVENILE GNOMES.

Baby Gnomes are known as 'GNOMEKINS' until they can walk and talk.
From then on, till adulthood they are known as 'GNOMELETS'.
Here we see a pair of Gnomelets playing in the safety of the entrance to a Gnome
cave or 'FOGOU' or 'WEEM'. They wear all in one button up overalls covered by
a soft furry jerkin held by a belt at the waist and play with simple but exquisitely
made hand crafted toys.

GNOME HOUSES AND HOMES

GNOME HABITATION

Originally Gnomes lived in excavated caves in banks called 'Fogou' or in some areas 'Weems'.

A little known fact is that long ago back in the mists of time, badgers who are related to weasels, polecats and stoats, were arboreal or tree dwelling animals and their lives were spent high in the treetops. Unfortunately, badgers are one of the few animals that suffer from acute vertigo.

The badgers noticed the Gnomes living in their cosy underground homes and moved in, gratefully giving up the arboreal life forever. In turn, the Gnomes, when they had recovered from the shock of finding they had an ever increasing number of large furry, and somewhat odiferous co-habitees, resolved to change their habitation. With a few exceptions where Gnomes still live underground, the Gnomes thus took to the trees. The excavations we now call badger setts are, in reality, ancient Gnome homes.

THE STARTER HOME

Apart from some newly wed Gnomes who live in the traditional Fogou, the basic Gnome 'starter home' is in the hollow of a tree. Knot holes are bored out and glazed. If not already present, ivy, the sacred plant of Gnomedom, is planted to ward off evil and conceal the home. Gnome homes start at ground level but as the Gnome family status rises over the years, they move to bigger and better homes higher up the tree. Hence the English saying 'to go up in the world' came from the Gnomes.

THE UPWARDLY MOBILE HOME

    Illustrated opposite is a beautifully situated Gnome home in the crux of a tall tree, in this case a tall straight Oak tree. The home is totally invisible from ground level. It catches the breeze in summer, and this combined with the dappled shade makes this a very desirable home. The home is reached from ground level by a series of cunningly concealed rope ladders. Over the years I have become somewhat of an expert at spotting these rope ladders which are the best clue to the presence of a Gnome home. The Gnomes know this too, and so take great pains to conceal them.

The homes themselves are warm and weatherproof, safe even in the most extreme weather and always made of natural materials, sourced locally. This means the architectural appearance may vary from area to area and regionally, depending on what is available. The home seen here is of a timber frame construction using oak for the main frame. Fixings are of hazel with the roof being constructed of ash with a straw thatching. Windows are glazed using small pieces of glass. This is the one material that Gnomes struggle with. The Gnome Forge Masters who make their iron and steel tools also work glass but the transportation makes it prohibitive. Small pieces of broken glass from bottles are therefore heated and re-formed locally to make the traditional diamond shaped lights that are typical of Gnome homes and much copied by humans in their cottages. The spaces between the timber framing in the walls is filled with clay, here a terra cotta coloured clay from the local river, reinforced with hair gathered from thorns and fences where animals have passed by. This is worked over a lattice of hazel twigs.

Note that Gnomettes rarely wear boots at home, preferring the traditional pink fluffy slippers.

THE MANSION GNOME HOME

This luxury Gnome home is at the top of the tree, concealed in mature ivy and hidden from view by its location in the crux of a mighty oak tree. The home is occupied by a large Gnome family group, possibly several generations. The house itself is a rambling, 'country manor' design with numerous added wings and extensions.

This home is reached through the hollow centre of the oak, a common practise with Gnomes. The hollow trees are often occupied by many other animals from owls to bats who, without exception tolerate, if not welcome, the comings and goings of the resident Gnome family. The entrance is always very well concealed at the base of the tree between the roots. Once inside there are ladders or steps cut into the sides of the cavity leading all the way up to the house at the top. The steps lead directly into a lobby or hall in the centre of the home. It is only because I had come to know and be trusted by our local Gnome population that they came to trust me enough to show me the home.

The home itself is of the usual timber frame construction of oak, fastened using hazel, with a clay and hair infill over a hazel lattice. The roof timbers are of ash and the roof tiles are made from pine cone segments, which due to their high resin content, tend to last a very long time. The pine gives the home a pleasant scented quality too. The roof is decorated with carved finials and ornamental barge boards which reflect the status of the Gnome family in residence. This, as in other constructed homes, has a wide outdoor terrace where the Gnomes can relax far away from prying eyes. There are many windows indicating a successful family that can afford the incredibly expensive window glass.

I have found these beautifully constructed homes all over the land, but unless you know what to look for, they are virtually impossible to find. A woodman I met recounted cutting down an ancient oak and finding a shattered home that had been in the top of the tree. He had put the bits of 'twigs' down to a crow's nest!

THE TOP OF THE RANGE GNOMANSION

THE NUTS, BERRIES
AND FLOWERS USED
FOR A VARIETY OF
PURPOSES INCLUDING
FOOD

NUTS

Gnomes consume a vast variety of nuts, so I have restricted this chapter to the nuts found on the Islands of Britain. These nuts are, however, found over the entire continent of Europe.

ASH Fraxinus exelsior:
Ash seeds are eaten by Gnomes much as we humans eat peanuts when relaxing with a drink at the end of a long hard day. They extract the seeds and roast them as a snack food. Ash is the wood used by Gnomes for the handles of their various tools such as axes and spades. They also use ash as their main fuel as it burns 'green,' meaning they can gather fire wood all year round without the necessity of stacking and 'drying' wood.

SWEET CHESTNUT Castanea sativa:
This is the basic ingredient of Gnome flour, and the main ingredient for porridge like food called 'GOLLENTA'.
They also roast the nuts then chop them up with their axes into bite sized chunks. The wood is highly prized in areas where there are termites, as they do not attack the wood.

HAZEL Corylus avellana:
This is arguably the most useful
plant known to Gnomes.

The wood is used in everything from fixings
in timber framed houses to holding down
thatch and forming lattice work for clay
infill. The poles are used for
ladders and climbing poles. Even
the ubiquitous 'snake stick' is hazel.
They also use it to make charcoal for their
iron forges.

The hazel nuts, known to the Gnomes as
'COBMATS' are the most prized
food of all. The nuts are ground down into a flour, the fat is
extracted to make the delicious Gnome butter, they make hazel milk, and the roasted
nuts have a large range of uses in Gnome cuisine.

The Gnomes store their hazel nuts in specially constructed silos in hollow trees. The
hollow is lined with a waterproof clay, then once the nuts have been stored the entrance
is sealed using the same clay then carefully camouflaged. This is one of the rare times
that Gnomes come into conflict with animals. Squirrels adore hazel nuts and seem to
be of the opinion that the Gnome silos of nuts are for their personal use. The stores are
vital to the Gnomes for their winter survival, and the squirrels are more than capable
of storing their own nuts, but prefer to be lazy! The Gnomes will not however accept
this and will fight for their nut stores.

Fortunately Gnomes will only fight by the Marquess of Gnomesberry rules, so happily, no one ever gets hurt!

WALNUT Junglans regia:
The walnuts when green resemble large green spotty plums. When picked in their green state they are pickled in delicately flavoured raspberry vinegar, a great Gnomish delicacy.

Ripened walnuts lose their fleshy surround to reveal the hard shell. The halved shells are much prized as cup like utensils. The nut kernels have many uses in Gnome cuisine, one of the favourites being walnut nut loaf served with wild horseradish.

OAK:
Oaks have many uses from wooden casks for beer and wine (as the wood is impervious to alcohol), to the acorns which have many uses.
Gnomes call acorns 'KORNMAT'. The acorns are ground up for food and roasted to make a form of coffee. I have not tried eating acorns for Gnomes have a digestive tract that is far more robust than ours. Plants that would poison and possibly kill humans are consumed with relish by Gnomes. Large numbers of these plants have the toxins removed by simple processes known to Gnomes for millennia.

THE COMMON OAK Quercus rober

THE HOLM OAK Quercus Ilex

THE SESSILE OAK Quercus petraea

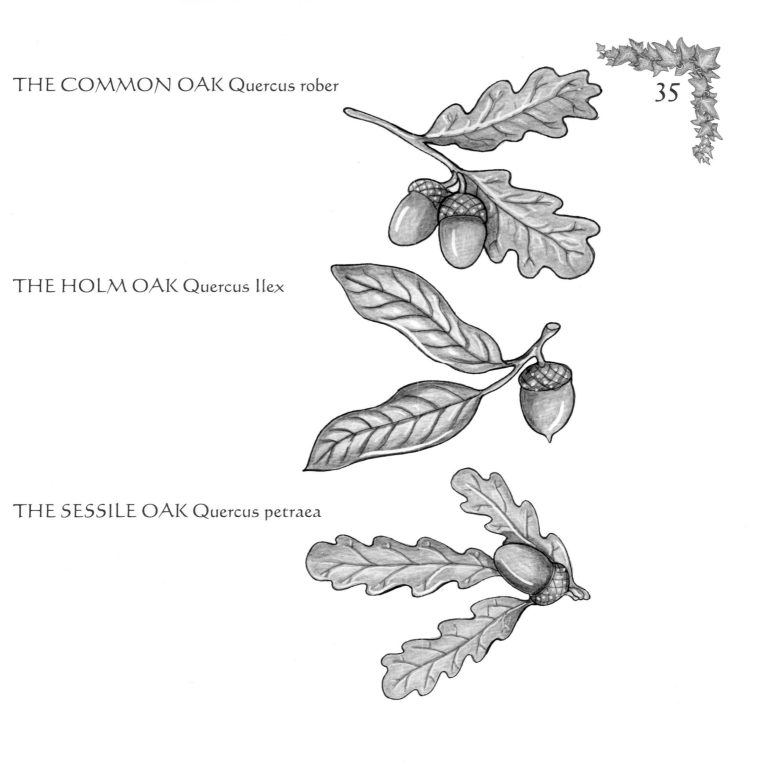

Apart from cutting up and sun drying food, which is problematic in wet humid climates, nuts are stored whole, then powdered using special stone mortars with long stone pestles known as 'POUNDING STONES'.

The pounding stone is beautifully fashioned from Preseli Blue Stone by expert Gnome masons. The implement is comprised of a deep cylindrical stone pot with a rounded bottom. The nuts are placed in the bottom and then pounded into a fine powder using the long heavy two handed pestle. The implement has to be perfectly made from flawless stone so it will withstand many years of heavy use without cracking or, more importantly, chipping which would taint the fine flour. The stone known to Gnomes as 'BLUEPOUND' is only found on the sides of craters on a range of ancient volcanoes in the far West of the country, known to the Gnomes as CAMBRIA .

The pounded nuts and seeds are put to many uses and the different flours are mixed to make a variety of loaves, cakes and biscuits, one of these being the hard dry biscuits carried by all Gnomes as emergency rations called 'G-Rations'. They are highly nutritious and will get Gnomes through the most severe times including the worst of winters. Roasted nuts and acorns are also powdered in the pounding stones to make a variety of stimulating drinks, more often than not served with roasted seeds or berries. I have heard tell that Gnomes collect milk from cows that are lying down chewing the cud but have never witnessed this.

Nut milk is a product made from hazel nuts and is extremely nutritious. Gnomekins are normally fed this as a supplement to breastfeeding. I have tried this hazel milk and can verify that it is delicious.

THE POUNDING STONE

BERRIES

Berries are, next to nuts, the most important nutritional source for Gnomes, and the following is a resume of the main berries consumed by them. A very good way to spot your local Gnomes is to conceal yourself near a ripe berry bush or plant and if you are patient you will probably get a glimpse of some berry hunting Gnomes.

BLACKBERRIES Rubus fructicosus:
One of the commonest fruits and often prepared with apple. Gnomes have great difficulty in harvesting the berries as they have to get through the tangle of prickly, thorny bramble to get to the fruits called PRICKLEBERRY by Gnomes.

CRANBERRY Vaccinium oxycoccus:
Mainly found on bogs these are very acid tasting berries, much loved by Gnomes who call them BITTERBERRY

BILBERRY Vaccinium myrtillus:
Found on moorland and mountains. The tangy
fruit is much prized as a rich source of vitamins.
Gnomes call these berries 'BAABERRY'

COWBERRY Vaccinium vitisidaea:
Once again a low growing shrub of
mountain and high ground. The berries
are extremely bitter but devoured with relish
by Gnomes who call them 'MOOBERRY'

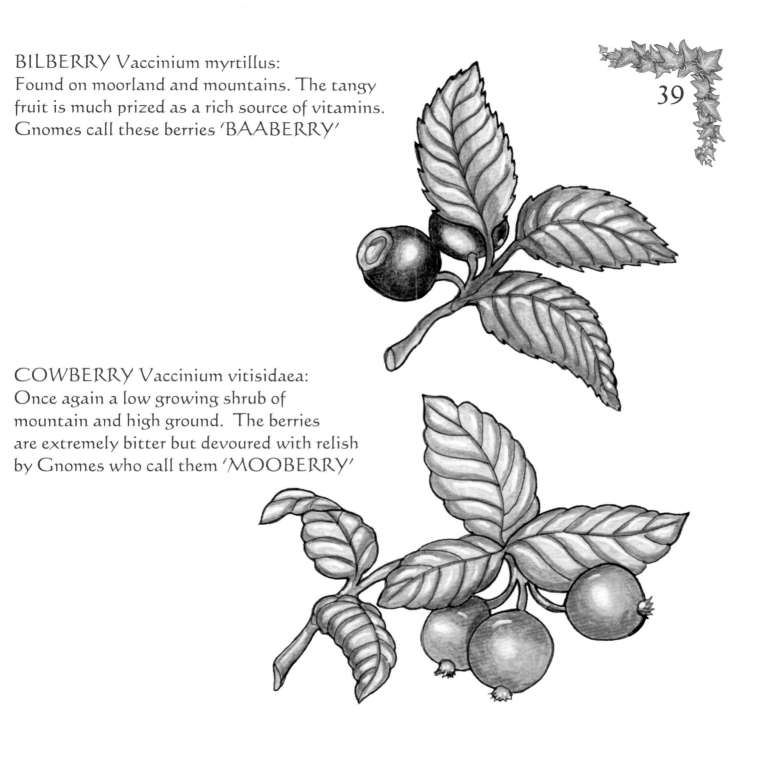

WILD STRAWBERRY Fragaria vesca:
Widespread berry found in hedgerows and woods,
these are the Gnomes favourite fruit. Commercial
strawberry farmers often lose large numbers of
strawberries to Gnomes, who gather on the
farms for great nights of strawberry
feasting. Gnomes call strawberries
'PARADISE BERRIES'.

CLOUDBERRY Rubus chamaemorus:
Found on bogs this low growing shrub
with its large yellow fruits is much craved
by Gnomettes during pregnancy. Called
'SUNBERRY' by Gnomes.

ELDER Sambucus nigra:
This small tree has hollow stems and is
used extensively by Gnomes for everything
from piping water to drainage and making
the traditional musical 'NOSEPIPE'.
The berries are used to make a heady
sweet wine which is drunk at Gnome
Weddings and celebrations like the New
Year on the Summer Solstice. Gnomes call
them 'WINEBERRY'.

RASPBERRY Rubus idaeus:
These berries are widespread in woods
and hedges. The North and West,
with their wetter climates, produce the
sweetest berries. They are made into a
soothing drink and a fine vinegar for
flavouring. Gnomes call them
'SWEETBERRY'.

THE GNOME STILL

Gnomes have very sophisticated methods of processing the foods they harvest. One of the most important Gnomes in the local clan is the one who is expert in brewing and distillation. Gnomes do not drink to excess but do however enjoy a drink, mainly at celebrations. The alcohol levels in these drinks is kept incredibly low by the Master Brewers.

The main occasions for the consumption of 'special' drinks are weddings, births and at the hugely popular Gnome's New Year Celebration which takes place at the start of the annual Gnome Calendar on the 21st of June, what we call the 'Summer Solstice'.

The stills are always set up in deep cover where fuel is plentiful and near a spring where the water is as pure as possible. The still itself is constructed by the Forge Master Gnomes who make all the Gnome metal tools and implements. The distillates are stored in stone bottles made in the Clay Country of Middle Anglia, what we would recognise as The Potteries.

The copper for the stills is mined in the Cambrian Mountains and transported by 'Porter Gnomes' to one of the three iron working centres on the mainland of Britain.

It must be said that the distillation process is for many purposes, and the least important is for alcoholic beverages. In fact the distillates are mainly used for the preservation of food. The Gnomes do not farm, nor do they have freezers, so they harvest when the food is in season and preserve it for future consumption.

THE DISTILLATION EXPERT

PLANTS EATEN BY GNOMES

Gnomes consume a huge variety of plants. Here are some of the more common varieties. Any of these favourites will attract the attention of Gnomes.

CHICKWEED Stellaria media: Common, eaten as a spring salad or boiled as a vegetable.

BORAGE Borago officinalis: Another Gnome staple, found on banks and in hedges. The young leaves are used in salads and also infused in water to make a refreshing drink. The flowers are used to brighten up salads and drinks.

MARSH MALLOW Althaea hirsuta: Up to four feet high, related to Mallow, it grows on coastal salt marshes. The dried powdered roots are much prized to make confectionery.

MALLOW Malva sylvestris:
The Common Mallow has several
uses. The fruits develop to resemble
small cakes that taste of peanuts. The
leaves are used in salads and as
medicinal poultices and a soothing
ointment is made from the roots.

FATHEN Chenopodium album:
This plant has seeds that are black and
shiny with a very high fat content. The
boiled leaves make a spinach like dish.

WHEAT, BARLEY AND RYE

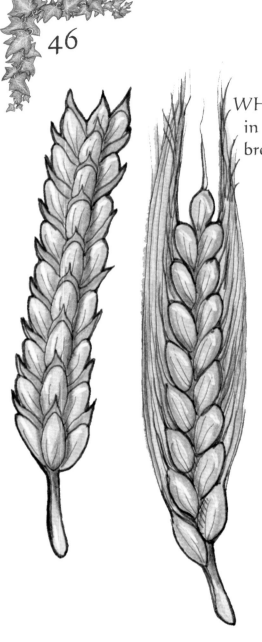

WHEAT: Grains are pounded into powder in a mortar to produce a flour for bread and pastry.

BARLEY: Used primarily in beer making but also when boiled with water produces barley water for Gnomelets.

RYE: Rye flour is used to make 'BLACK GNOMBREAD'.
This is only eaten on special occasions such as the Solstice festivals and the Gnome Pilgrimage when Gnomes carry the bread for sustenance on their trek to the Sacred Mountain in Cambria (Wales).

FORAGING METHODS AND TECHNIQUES

Gnomes have developed very sophisticated methods of preserving their food supplies which consist of, as far as I can ascertain, nuts, berries, and fruit.

The only 'meat' they eat is fish, namely minnows from fresh water and sand eels from the coast. These are never stored but eaten fresh. The Gnomes tell of a Clan of Gnomes over the big waters in a place called Franconia where they eat slugs and snails with wild garlic, and would you believe, the legs of frogs! The Gnomes on the Islands of Britannia look upon this practise with great revulsion.

I have found no evidence of Gnomes eating or using fungi, so the traditional image of a gnome sitting on a poisonous Fly Agaric Toadstool is entirely fantastical!

Several species of fruit and vegetable cultivated by us humans are greatly prized by Gnomes. There are in fact three fruits they cannot resist: which are Plums, Apples and Pears, then two vegetables they seek out which are Carrots and Sugar Beet.

The Gnomes gather slightly more than they need of these crops. They eat their fill of fresh fruit and vegetables when in season then make stores of the remainder once they have been skilfully preserved.

Here we see a pair of Gnomes collecting low hanging plums using a hazel collecting stick - a pole which is held vertical by one Gnome while the other shins up to get at the plums.

50 Gnomes tend to carry everything, as the terrain where they live can be extremely difficult at times. However, they do use a small cart to transport heavier items such as apples. These little carts are most commonly seen in the flatter areas of Anglia. To see a pair of Gnomes with one of their exquisitely constructed and painted little carts is a rare and special treat. Apples are highly prized by Gnomes. They are stored, wrapped in dock leaves, in underground SOUTERRAINS.

Gnomes use just two of the root crops grown by farmers, namely sugar beet and carrots. The carrots are extremely important as Gnomes require excellent night vision. Professor Retsof's research has shown Gnomes vision is similar to cats and they can see the full colour spectrum, including infra red and ultra violet. To maintain this they consume large quantities of carrots. Carrots are uprooted using three sheer legs and a block and tackle. (Three little holes where there is a gap in a row of carrots is a sure sign of Gnome activity.)

The other root crop the Gnomes use is the white pointed root of the sugar beet plant which is grown for commercial sugar production. The root weighs up to a kilo and contains about seventeen percent sugar. Gnomes will remove an individual beet then pulp it down and distil the sugar out of the pulp, which they then use as a preservative.

Sugar Beet:
This crop is mainly grown in the flat arable farming areas in the East of the Country.

One of the main dangers Gnomes face whilst fishing for their favourite minnow delicacy is pike-attack. This huge fearsome predatory fish, the 'shark' of fresh water takes birds, voles, other fish, frogs and really relishes Gnomes. So the sight of a large pike really does frighten the daylights out of Gnomes.

Sand eels are the great Gnome delicacy, comparable I suppose to the human delicacy of Caviar. The Gnomes catch the sand eels at low tide by drumming their feet on the sand by the entrance to a sand eel burrow, which brings the curious eels to the surface. The eels are then eaten fresh with raspberry vinegar. So absorbed do Gnomes get 'drumming' for eels, they forget about the tide, and I have frequently seen little Gnomes running frantically ahead of the incoming sea.

THE THREE DYE COLOURS
USED BY GNOMES

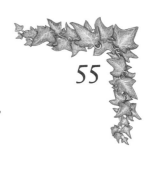

There are three plants the Gnomes use to produce their coloured clothing, a red, yellow and blue.

MADDER Rubia peregrina:
This is the most important dye yielding plant in Gnomedom. It is found near rocky coasts. The roots of Madder produce the red dye so important to the production of the Red Gnome Hats, or 'Hattons' sometimes called 'Bonnet Rouge'.

DYERS GREENWEED Genista tinctoria:
Produces a yellow dye, and combined with woad produces various shades of green.

WOAD Isatis tinctoria:
The leaves are crushed and boiled to get the blue dye. The Romans when they arrived at Dover thought the Ancient Britons were wearing this as war paint, but truth to tell they were blue with cold after hanging around on the White Cliffs for hours to greet the new wave of immigrants.

GNOMES AND THEIR INTERACTION WITH WILDLIFE

Gnomes are extremely beneficial for wildlife. One service they perform is the burial of dead animals. Animals that die naturally are skinned and the pelts are used to make the leather clothing and boots the Gnomes wear. This is why when you walk in a wood, you never see any dead animals. This service alone is hugely beneficial to wildlife as it prevents the spread of disease. Gnomes will tend to wounded animals too, dressing wounds and dosing sick animals with restorative potions.

Foxes take great pleasure in making Gnomes jump by suddenly appearing and staring at them. The foxes will not, however, harm a Gnome. I have actually seen young Gnomelets curled up asleep in the sun with a litter of fox cubs, the parent fox standing watch over the peacefully sleeping youngsters. This applies to all the mammals and birds. I have seen buzzards swooping down then pulling up again when they realise that they are swooping down on a Gnome. I personally suspect that the animals all recognise the red Gnome 'Hatton' and respect it. This reminds me of the Masai on the African plains: lions recognise their red 'shukas' and leave them alone.

The incredible fierce little hunters stoats, weasels and polecats have a very friendly relationship with Gnomes, almost like dogs and humans.

The genetic makeup of Gnomes means that they have a complete natural immunity to all kinds of venomous bites, be it from snakes, spiders or scorpions.

Snakes are incredibly fond of Gnomes, like dogs to humans and just like dogs, they try to lick the faces of Gnomes as an expression of love and devotion. Unfortunately snakes suffer from incredibly bad breath because they eat so infrequently. Gnomes, who are naturally clean and not at all keen on nasty smells, find the slobbering of their legless chums quite unacceptable. Thus the reason that Gnomes are nearly always seen with a forked walking stick. It is called a SNAKE STICK and its purpose is to fend off over affectionate snakes.

A Gnome who forgot his Snake Stick.

Gnomes feel most at home when they have the cover of vegetation. They therefore will frequent shrubberies, hedges, woodland and tend to avoid wide open spaces like close cropped meadows. If they have to cross a wide meadow or field they will often wait till it is dark, or they will work their way round in the boundary hedge.

Where there are open areas they must cross frequently, Gnomes excavate under the surface, normally some several feet down, constructing permanent runs or tunnels.

The rate at which Gnomes dig their tunnels is absolutely amazing. They make that arch tunneller, the mole, look slow.

One of the problems with these tunnels is that Gnomes will often break unexpectedly into rabbit burrows, much to the surprise and irritation of the local rabbit population. This is not such a problem for moles as they tend to tunnel closer to the surface and their tunnels are far smaller.

Fortunately the rabbits and Gnomes co-exist very peacefully so this is not a major problem. Rabbits, when they make a nest in their burrows for their young to be born in, line the nest with incredibly soft belly fur to keep the young warm and snug. This fur is highly prized by the Gnomes to spin and knit into their warm winter clothes.

Gnomes and birds have a very close relationship. Gnomes will frequently travel huge distances on the backs of large migrating birds like the Whooper Swans and Trumpeter Swans, or the larger migrating geese. Professor Retsof's research has shown that this is the way that Gnomes have spread so far and wide around the Globe.

It is also a known fact that birds and Gnomes have a very sophisticated relationship, to the point they can actually communicate with each other. This mutually beneficial relationship has greatly improved both the Gnomes and birds chances of having a fruitful, safe life.

Birds communicate with Gnomes, warning them of danger and more importantly acting as their aerial spotters of foods to gather, be they nuts and berries, even field crops that are ripe for harvest. Birds will also warn Gnomes of danger. Their warning calls to Gnomes are always heeded.

Try it yourself. Walk into a wood and listen. You will hear the alarm calls of jays who will have spotted you. Magpies also warn of danger, while other birds such as pigeons will keep quiet when danger lurks. As you enter a wood, listen for the cooing of pigeons and doves, their silence means they have either seen you or something else is there that worries them!

Birdsong is the primary inspiration for Gnome music. Gnome musicians develop tunes inspired by the song of birds, especially the thrush family.

Where there is a shortage of nest sites, the Gnomes will excavate holes in trees or cliffs to aid the birds.

The low lying Fen Country in the east of the country the Gnomes call Anglia, has its own Gnome Clan who specialise in living alongside the many miles of drains, ditches, cuts, rivers and canals. Many of the workers who maintain the waterway tell of encounters with these wetland Gnomes.

These Gnomes almost always live underground in their excavated 'Weems' as the Fen country habitations are called. Some will go up into willows to build houses but willows are notoriously weak, and will break in the high wind that can howl across the flat Fens, often plunging home and inhabitants into the cold waterways, so snug underground houses are much favoured.

I spent many months on the Fen studying the population of Gnomes. On one remarkable occasion I saw a solitary Gnomette working a drain with a short handled net. At first I thought she was fishing then realised she was catching tiny frogs that had recently metamorphosed from tadpoles. I was horrified at first, convinced I had found a frog eating Gnome clan. But I was much relieved to discover that she was performing one of the Gnomes' major services to the Fen - she was catching small frog-lets and transporting them to other less populated waterways, so ensuring a healthy population. Needless to say, large numbers of frogs in one place attracts a lot of predators like herons, storks, cranes, and otters.

Otters incidentally will use old Gnome Weems as holts to rear their young. However, they never disturb lived in Gnome Weems. As the top predator of the waterway, and arguably the most intelligent, otters get on extremely well with Gnomes, who in turn appreciate the otters playful nature.

THE LIFESTYLE, CLOTHING AND HABITS OF GNOMES

THE GNOME RED HAT
OR HATTON OR BONNET ROUGE

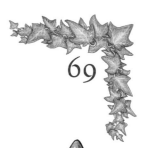

The Gnome hats are made by specialist hat makers, what we would call milliners. However this would imply they made ornamental hats but in fact these Gnome specialists only make the one design of hat.

The hat makers live in traditional centres, of which there are eight in what the Gnomes call Britannia. These centres are called HATTONS in: Aberdeen and Angus in Scotland or Caledonia, then in England or Anglia, six centres, all called HATTON, in Derbyshire, London, Lincolnshire, Shropshire, Cheshire, and Warwickshire. In Wales, or as the Gnomes call it Cambria, the only hat making centre is in a place called Llantwit Major in the Vale of Glamorgan. All these centres have now got the name of HATTON (except of course in Wales), but this proves a link with Gnomes that goes right back to the Doomsday Book!

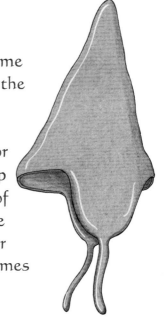

The HATTON is always the same design, and always the same colour but varying in shades of red - with one exception which is the Gnomes of Sherwood.

The conical hat has a pair of built in ear flaps with chinstraps for cold and windy weather. Normally the ear pieces are folded up inside the hat out of sight, and only used in the most extremes of weather. The flaps slightly impair the Gnomes hypersensitive hearing so are only deployed when absolutely necessary. Their main purpose is to prevent chilblains to the ears, something Gnomes are very vulnerable to.

The Gnome 'HATTON' is made of a mixed yarn spun from a variety of plant fibres to give it stiffness and longevity, with several animal wools including rabbit 'down' on the inside as insulation. The secret formula for this yarn is only known to the Gnomes from the Centres I have listed earlier and handed down from generation to generation. The hats lose their stiffness after a few months and become soft and comfortable. The Gnomes use special tools to make the hat, which is formed on a 'TURNCONE' using a 'WOGGLETOG' which give the hat its classic shape and very tight weave.

Gnome hats or HATTONS are transported to all the regions by specialist porters from the hat making clans, who are known as 'SHERPAGNOMES'.

The hats are carried on their backs in specially made thong cradles.

These SHERPAGNOMES have a characteristic stoop from the long hours of carrying the heavy loads of hats.

THE GNOME FORGE MASTERS

Gnomes use a variety of tools and implements, readily recognisable to us humans, from knives and axes to spades, shovels and scythes. All the implements to our eyes are tiny but on inspection you will see they are exquisitely made.

There are three main Gnome forge centres that have been there so long, the human place names reflects the original Gnome activity in the area.
These are:
IRONVILLE, Derbyshire in England, or ANGLIA to Gnomes.
FORGEHAMMER, Cwmbran, in South Wales or CAMBRIA
FORGANDENNY, Perth, in Scotland or CALEDONIA.

The traditional Gnome Forges are well concealed in hollowed out caves at the bottom of sheltered banks. The smoke is ducted away, usually through hollow trees above the forge or through a complex series of tunnels in the bank above the forge. They are so well constructed that it is virtually impossible to locate a forge by the smell of smoke.

Gnomettes are the 'Forgemasters', and are consummate experts in forging implements. They usually work wearing a protective jerkin, which is of a far thicker leather than the norm. The fire is kept fed with charcoal and the bellows worked by a Gnome assistant. Once again the Gnome Clans who specialise in metalwork are totally dedicated to this task and this is not undertaken anywhere else on these islands.

All Gnome metalwork, from brass buckles to copper stills, is undertaken at these centres. Their products are transported by 'SHERPAGNOMES' like those who transport the Hattons.

A GNOMETTE FORGE-MASTER FASHIONS
AN IRON IMPLEMENT IN A GNOME FORGE FOGOU

HOUSEWORK AND CHORES

Gnomes tend to do the majority of housework .

Gnomettes look after the Gnomekins almost exclusively till they grow into Gnomelets when parental duties are shared.

Gnomes pair for life and their relationships are lifelong and faithful.

It is not an uncommon sight to see a Gnomette relaxing in a rocking chair (rocking chairs are a Gnome invention going back to the dawn of time and copied by humans) with a drink of herbal tea while the Gnome presses the laundered clothes using a small iron that contains glowing bits of charcoal for heat. Gnomes have a fine space between their two front teeth, and this gap is used to spray water on the laundry to moisten it when ironing.

This pair of Gnomes are relaxing at the entrance to a cave or FOGOU. Their home was in fact in the tree above but the south facing cave was ideal to relax in and catch the late winter sun. Washing of clothes is always done in the local streams where great care is taken to wash downstream of where the Gnomes draw their fresh water. They use a soap derived from walnut fat blended with a mixture of fragrant herbs.

One of the things that most impressed me about Gnomes is their extreme cleanliness, bordering on the fastidious. Gnome latrines are specially built so they fertilize the local plants and emit no odours whatsoever.

GNOME ABLUTIONS

Gnomes are very clean and believe in regular bathing. In fact they bathe with great delight once every year, just before the twenty first of June, the Gnome New Year, which is always celebrated with a huge party.

Bathing is ALONE, for Gnomes are extremely shy and modest and the bath is taken in a secluded, hidden pool on a stream or rivulet, normally close to the source. Gnomes will travel some distance from their home to bathe as the right water is essential to them - neither too hard nor too soft. The 'bath' lasts for many hours, with the Gnomes repeatedly scrubbing themselves with herbal soaps.

Professor Retsof has established that Gnomes, unlike we humans, do not have sweat glands, so they do not perspire like us. Body odour is therefore not a problem to Gnomes. The other extreme of this is Gnomes have to regulate their body heat very carefully. So as a Gnome watcher, you should always look for Gnomes in shady places - in woodland, under banks and hedgerows or on overcast days.

Another fact about Gnomes, whence they differ from us, is that they are always slightly rotund, the body fat acting as insulation to cool the blood. The Gnomes' ears are always large, and detailed examination has revealed that their ears, apart from giving them hearing some twelve times more efficient than our own, also cool their blood, acting as a pair of little radiators. Their hearing is also able to detect both ultra sound and infra sound. They are in effect perfectly tuned for life in the 'wild'.

THE BATH

THE CURIOSITY OF GNOMES

Gnomes are intensely curious about humans, much as we are about species close to us like the gorillas. The first time I realised this, was when we had friends to stay for a short holiday at our remote Welsh home. Unusually for that part of the world, we were in the midst of a long hot dry summer.

Our friend's eighteen year old daughter was taking great delight in spending the long hot days sunbathing in a bikini on the lawn . My wife, passing the window, looked out and noticed movements in a rambling rose. Close inspection revealed at least eight Gnomes, there might have been more, peeking out from their concealment in various bushes and shrubs. They were watching the girl on the lawn with intense curiosity, and the reason for their interest was apparent - somebody was outdoors in what appeared to be their underwear (bearing in mind that Gnomes are extremely modest in each other's company). Sunbathing at this remote place in the hills was entirely new to them.

Wildlife in general is much the same, all animals in the wild regard humans as dangerous, and often with good reason. However, if you remain in the same place for a long time - sometimes this takes years - the local wildlife will come to see you as benign and start to relax in your presence. That's provided you leave them alone! Once you have become part of that wildlife's daily routine you will be able to sit quietly in a garden or a wood and have animals come right up to you. This, I discovered, applied to Gnomes as well and eventually their curiosity got the better of them and they made contact with me. This is how I came to garner so much information about Gnomes, much of which was told to me by the local Gnome Patriarchs; Hieronymous Goodfellow and Musprat Goodfellow, through whom I learnt the language of Gnomes. I have heard this referred to as "Gnomish" but according to the Gnomes it is called 'GNO', so they are in fact the people of GNO.

CURIOUS GNOMES

Research has found that Gnomes excite considerable interest in animals both wild and domestic. This interest is entirely benign, and never, as far as we can tell, results in any form of violence towards Gnomes. Our very large German Shepherd dogs were not only curious of Gnomes, but seemed to derive great pleasure being in their company.

Have you ever noticed your pet dog or cat staring intently out of the window, either in daylight or at night, but when you look yourself there is nothing visible to be seen? More than likely you are 'seeing' the first evidence that you have Gnomes resident in or near your garden.

Similarly you can get the feeling that someone is watching you, but there is no-one to be seen? Look around, but very slowly (and don't make it obvious you are doing so or else they will take cover). Look into deep shade, in shrubs or under bushes, because more than likely, there will be one or more Gnomes silently watching you.

Gnomes do not appear particularly moved by Gnome statues in gardens. However our research shows that gardens with discreetly placed Gnome statues are seen as more benign environments by the Gnomes themselves. It has long been a tradition in Britain to leave out saucers of bread and milk for hedgehogs. In fact hedgehogs far prefer dog food left out for them and usually let the Gnomes have the bread and milk, which they adore.

Gnomes do not however like the smell of smoke, especially from tobacco. It triggers a panic response as fire is one of the causes of Gnome mortality. Being small, they cannot easily escape from forest or heath fires, so the very smell of smoke will cause much alarm.

Gnomes for the most part travel on foot, and tend to stay within their territorial boundaries. These boundaries, like for all foraging species of animals, tend to encompass what they need to survive, namely food and water sources.

A Gnome territory has perfect population numbers so as not to upset the local balance of nature. This can cause the odd local dispute with neighbouring clans but is ritually settled as you will see later on.

However, long distance travel is sometimes undertaken and is usually by boat or by air on the backs of large migrating birds.

Gnomes that live in the forests or woods have evolved a fascinating method of rapid travel. This entails climbing into the tree tops and swinging from tree to tree on long vines, be that honeysuckle stems, ivy or other trailing creepers. They have, over the centuries, perfected this technique so that they make it look easy as they swoop from tree to tree like tiny trapeze artists. This swinging through the trees is normally silent but occasionally they let out a cry when they misjudge their swing.

The author Edgar Rice Burrows was walking through a woods one day when he heard just such a cry. Looking up into the canopy, he spotted a little Gnome swinging rapidly from tree to tree, squeaking with exhilaration. This is probably the moment that he was inspired to write his famous book about a man living amongst the animals in the jungle.

There is nothing quite so thrilling as going into a wild wood to see the swinging Gnomes swooping from tree to tree with supreme skill and accuracy.

Skilfully swinging from tree to tree......

Sometimes......

TRAVEL ON WATER

Apart from Riverine and Marshland Gnomes who use various methods to travel on their watery worlds, the Gnomes cross the oceans in specially built sailing boats. This is the way the Gnomes first came to the islands they call Britannia, across the water they call the Northern Ocean from Norway . The boats are in effect a hollowed out log or DUGOUT, sometimes with outriggers for stability.

They have a sail and oars and are steered by using a long steering oar, used as a rudder. They choose their crossing times very carefully to avoid the worst of the weather. Gnomes believe that the weather is controlled by the moon, the extremes always being round and about the full moon. The extremely violent weather is when there is a full moon at the Solstice. I have kept records for some thirty years now and I, too, have found that extremes in weather seem to coincide with the full moon. Nevertheless these crossings, undertaken by small family groups, are extremely dangerous. We will never know how many Gnomes perish on the high seas and crossings like these are only undertaken when absolutely necessary.

Gnomes, of course, were the first to visit, and settle, in North America, which they refer to as New Gnomeland. The crossing was made from Britannia (the British Isles), to the Island of Fire (Iceland), thence onto Frozenland (Greenland) and onto what we call Canada, then on down the Coast to the Eastern States of America.

These sailing epics were quite incredible when you see the size of their boats. They were without doubt the first to cross the Atlantic, long before we humans attempted it. The other methods of travelling over water are Coracles, or more correctly 'GORACLES'.

THE SEAGOING GNOME BOAT OR DUGOUT

There is a clover leaf, the symbol of protection, on the sail of this dugout so it is probably crossing the dangerous sea between Britannia and Hibernia (Britain and Ireland)

AIR TRAVEL

Gnomes have been 'flying' for as long as birds have been migrating. This, to them, is the safest way to travel. The Gnomes ride on the backs of large migrating birds, like swans and geese, the most notable being the Bewick's and Trumpeter swans. There is no evidence however of Gnomes riding on birds of prey. This 'piggy back' flying seems to be mainly on the backs of swans and geese. Japanese Gnomologists tell of Gnomes travelling on the backs of migrating cranes, and there have been many sightings of Gnomes travelling up through Europe on the backs of the European stork. This is probably what gave rise to the tales of storks delivering babies. It was probably Gnomes sliding off the stork's back after long haul flights from places far to the south of Europe.

This is certainly the way the majority of the Gnome population of the British Isles came to be here and, from records from the various wetland reserves, still continues today with regular sightings of Gnomes arriving on the Autumn swan migrations from the far north of Europe.

The Swans would appear to gain considerable benefit from the Gnomes extraordinary navigation skills. The broad backs of the swans and geese and their exceptionally well insulated feathers makes the flights extremely comfortable for the Gnomes. Judging by their distribution on the birds in a 'V' formation, great care is taken to distribute their weight evenly between the birds in the flight.

Some of the most spectacular sights I have ever seen are the arrival of the Bewick's swans, each with their complement of Gnome passengers.

GNOMES ON BEWICK'S SWANS

THE FORMAL GREETING AND THE CHALLENGE

Gnomes are very formal in their behaviour. There is none of the over familiarity that is now so prevalent in our society. Gnomes treat each other with great respect, and one of the keys to getting to know your local Gnome population is respect. In fact you must always treat them with the greatest deference. Never treat a Gnome like an old friend until you have known him or her for at least four years.

When two Gnomes meet, they perform the greeting ritual. This is the removal of HATTONS (hats), which are then moved up and down in greeting. This is accompanied with formal inquiries about family and health, which being Gnomes, is always positive.

THE FORMAL GREETING

Within the individual Gnome Clans the formal ceremony of the HATTON has been simplified to a simple gesture. This is performed by holding up the first two fingers of the right hand to form a 'V' which represents the inverted Hatton. This gesture of friendly greeting is then emphasised by a rapid and prolonged up and down movement of the hand. Gnomes when meeting will always use this gesture while enquiring as to the others health.

In Britain, the human population has adopted this gesture as one of deep respect and warm greeting. Should you be visiting Britain and someone makes this gesture at you, he is in fact courteously greeting you and etiquette demands you reply in kind whilst smiling broadly.

Because Gnomes live by foraging, they have of necessity well defined local, clan and national boundaries. When a Gnome strays out of his or her territory, they are normally greeted by the threat display of the GNAKA.

This is a highly ritualised dance comprising of hand movements and grotesque facial distortions to deter the intruder from straying further.

However, should the GNAKA fail to settle the dispute the Gnomes will settle their argument with a duel using the ancient Gnome martial art called GUDO. This is a ritualised fight using sticks of wild celery. The first Gnome to lose his hat or Hatton is deemed to be the loser. Thus disputes are settled without any real harm being done to the combatants.

SACRED SITES
AND PILGRIMAGE

GNOMENHIRS

Wherever there are Gnomes, there are their sacred sites. Gnomes believe in the spirit world, the world where their ancestors dwell. These sites are visited to make offerings to, and communicate with, their long gone ancestors. On the British Isles there are four main types of sacred sites. The first of these are the 'GNOMENHIR' or 'Standing Stones' which were erected in the time the Gnomes call the "Dream Time". They are situated at the confluence of Ley Lines and are often visited by the Gnomes to renew their energy.

GNOMETORS

Piled and balanced boulders in the Southwest of Anglia (England) and on the northern moors are the sites where Gnomes believe their ancestors spirits congregate. These are only visited during the annual Pilgrimage, or PILGNOMAGE season.

DOLGNOMEN

This is the closest thing that Gnomes have to a human church. It is in the space between the three upright stones under the shelter of the covering stone that Gnomes congregate to perform the rituals that they believe help them remain mysterious and largely unseen by the human population. Evidence of use by Gnomes is the presence of small piles of cockle shells at the foot of the largest stone.

GNOMEHENGE

Great standing stones in groups of three called TRILIGNOMES, were erected, like the pyramids, thousands of years ago to celebrate the solstice. Gnomehenge on Salisbury Plain was the Canterbury of Sites but has been abandoned because of excessive human interference.

THE STONE OF GNOME AND THE SACRED MOUNTAIN

Our home in Wales, or as the Gnomes call it "Cambria", was in a valley below a high, round topped mountain called the "Frenni Fawr" (pronounced VRENY VOWER) , which means the Big Frenni. It is on this hill that is set the mysterious 'STONE OF GNOME'. This makes the Frenni, the Sacred Mountain of Gnomedom. Like the Rosetta Stone, this stone itself bears a strange inscription in the GNO Script .

It is quite by chance that I found the stone as it is incredibly well concealed and only some 50 cm's or 20 inches high. The inscription is very clear, so I took a photo of the inscription and sent it to Professor Retsof at the Institute of Gnomology in Munchen Gnomebach.

The good Professor immediately flew to Wales. Together we climbed the mountain and he examined the stone that is well concealed amongst the heather. He then used his divining rods to examine the forces below the hill and found that all the local Ley lines converged at the exact point where the stone was set.

The deciphering of this strange inscription became an obsession with both of us. It took the Professor many years before he finally deciphered the stone, which in turn gave him, and the Institute, the ability to understand the mysterious language of GNO.

It is by an extraordinary piece of luck that we happened to be living below the Frenni, and our valley was the home of the Gnome Clan known as the Goodfellows. It was through the 'habituation ' of this small Clan of Gnomes, and the deciphering of the "Stone of Gnome", that I managed to communicate with them and so learn their language and traditions.

THE PILGNOMAGE

Above the house we had a wild upland meadow, filled with wild flowers and orchids that was only cut once a year. This meadow was on what was a shoulder of the Frenni Fawr. I had been watching a fox with a pair of cubs hunting for voles in the grassland. The vixen would listen intently, then jump, thumping her fore paws down then suddenly plunge her head into the grass and come up with a vole, which would be quickly eaten. As I watched the vixen hunting through the grass tussocks, I noticed a movement right at the top end of the meadow.

I trained my binoculars onto the spot and was absolutely amazed to see a small group of Gnomes walking up along the ridge at the top of the meadow. Over the next few days I kept a watch on the top of the meadow and was intrigued to see dozens, if not hundreds, of Gnomes progressing up the hill.

Research has revealed that once every several years, at an appointed time - we are still trying to establish when - there is a Pilgrimage or Pilgnomage from all over the British Isles, and further still from Europe and North America to the Frenni, where the Ancient Stone of Gnome is venerated. Each pilgrim, or pilgnome as they prefer to be called, carries a cockle shell on his or her belt to indicate they are on the pilgnomage. They climb the north side of the mountain, then circle the stone some dozen times before descending on the south side, their obligation fulfilled. The majority of Gnomes merely walk the route, whilst others, as marks of devotion, will walk with a sack of rocks on their backs, or crawl the entire route on their knees, some even go so far as to walk with gravel in their boots. The ancient route is way marked with tiny arrows incised into boulders and stones along the path.

THE TWENTY FOUR PILGNOME STOPS ON THE ROUTE TO THE STONE OF GNOME

1: Nine Gnomes
2: Gnometorr Steps
3: Great Gnometor
4: Glastongnome Tor
5: Gnomebury Hill
6: Cissygnome Ring
7: Frenni Fawr
8: Wittergnome Clump
9: Four Gnome Stones
10: Gnomeclee Hill
11: Blue Gnome Cave
12: Gnome Low Stone Circle
13: Gnomewell Crag
14: Swingnome Circle
15: Whitegnome Cave
16: Brimgnome Rocks
17: Gnometrodden Stones
18: St Gnomeburts Cave
19: Gnomemoraig Stone Circle
20: Gnomehead Stone Circle
21: Gnomeable Stone Circle
22: Brown Gnome Hill Gnomen
23: Beaghgnome Stone Circle
24. Gnomedon

THE GRAND COUNCIL OF GNOMES

This is a portrait of the Grand Council of Gnomes for the West of Cambria. It was these diminutive gentlemen who made this Guide to Gnomes possible. The Gnome Clan of the West Cambria is called the Goodfellow Clan and these four are, from left to right: Tertius Goodfellow, Hieronymus Goodfellow, Musprat Goodfellow and Bonadventure Goodfellow. This Clan is the Guardian of the Stone of Gnome.

THE NEW YEAR CELEBRATION

As previously mentioned, the Gnome New Year is on the 21st of June, the Summer Solstice. This is celebrated with a great party that lasts for a full twenty four hours! There is dancing and feasting, including the traditional hazel nut and plum pie and fruit cake. The music is provided by a three piece Group playing the drum, nosepipe and auger shell. The Dance is always held in a woodland glade far from prying eyes.

Gnomes sketched
near the River Till
in Lincolnshire.

Dancing
Gnome

Hand axe or
Hatchet

THE DISTRIBUTION
OF GNOMES

THE BRITISH ISLES

The Gnomes of the British Isles are divided into four Countries. They refer to Britain as BRITANNIA, which is comprised of CALEDONIA (Scotland), ANGLIA (England), CAMBRIA (Wales) and HIBERNIA (Ireland).

They call the countries the FOUR REALMS.

There is no King Gnome as some believe, rather a Grand Councils of Gnomes who administer the regions.

However, the Gnomes do tell of a King of Gnomes who lives somewhere in the Alps.

The Gnomes are divided into many Clans and Sub-Clans.

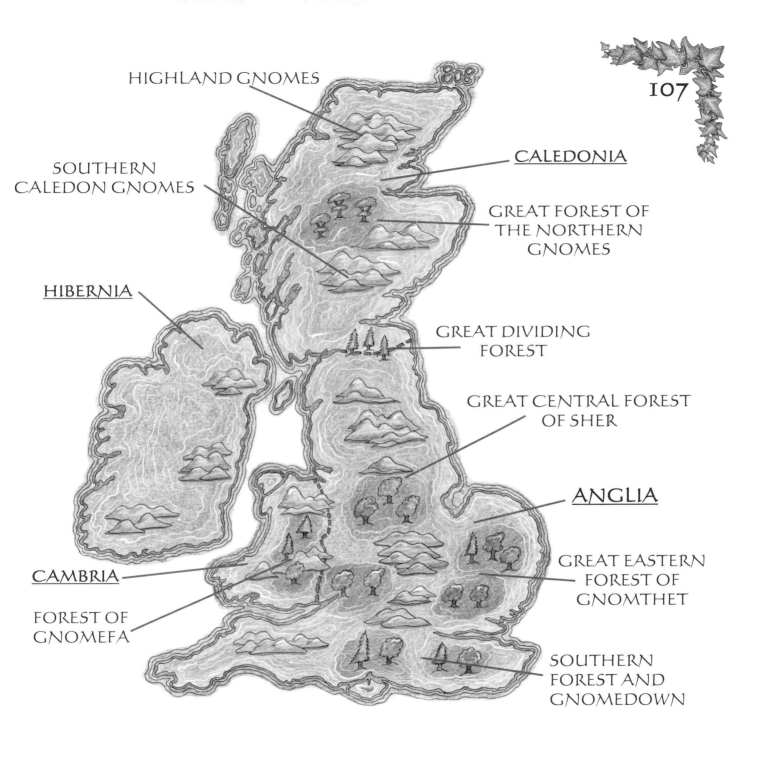

HIGHLAND GNOMES

SOUTHERN
CALEDON GNOMES

HIBERNIA

CAMBRIA

FOREST OF
GNOMEFA

CALEDONIA

GREAT FOREST OF
THE NORTHERN
GNOMES

GREAT DIVIDING
FOREST

GREAT CENTRAL FOREST
OF SHER

ANGLIA

GREAT EASTERN
FOREST OF
GNOMTHET

SOUTHERN
FOREST AND
GNOMEDOWN

WETLAND GNOMES OF THE EAST OF ANGLIA
GNOMUS ANGLIENSIS BOGTROTTICUS

These Gnomes live on and around the large marshlands, lakes and slow moving rivers found mainly in the East and South West of Anglia. They have a preference for these areas as human interference is minimal, and they are highly adapted to the areas they live in.

For the most part their homes are in the cavities of willow trees or underground.

Where there are large swathes of lily pads, the Gnomes have developed a technique of moving rapidly from leaf to leaf, their weight being evenly distributed by wearing special lily-paddles attached to their boots. It is quite extraordinary to see a Gnome speeding across a stretch of water, from lily pad to lily pad, without getting even slightly wet.

The deadly pike is always a lurking threat in these still, tranquil waters, so speed is essential. The nets they carry are used to catch minnows which are their staple protein in the wetland areas. This is the rare exception to what is the usual all-vegetarian Gnome diet.

WETLAND GNOME
GNOMUS ANGLIENSIS BOGTROTTICUS

WETLAND GNOMES

Gnomes who inhabit the wetter regions have several methods of crossing watercourses without getting wet. A common practise is the use of long stilts. These are often hidden in undergrowth near favoured crossing points, for any Gnome passing to use to cross the water.

One of the major setbacks of stilts is, in the East, the deep mud at the bottom of the watercourse, and of course, where streams and rivers flow from the hills, the danger of unseen rocks tripping up the unwary Gnome. This can be very dangerous for Gnomes, as to end up face down in deep water with their legs strapped to long poles can result in disaster. They therefore proceed with extreme caution.

The stilts are an excellent clue as to whether there are Gnomes near a particular river or watercourse.

III

SOUTHERN COMMUTER GNOMES
GNOMUS ANGLIENSIS COMMUTATUS

In the Southern Region of Anglia there are several Gnome Clans who have become known as the Commuter Gnomes.   Because of the Gnomes fascination with all things human, they have abandoned the traditional Gnome belt and pouch for brief cases to carry their essentials for foraging, namely sandwiches, knives and string. They have also replaced their traditional snake sticks with colourful umbrellas.   Their dress is still the same but for one glaring difference. They adorn their necks with colourful pieces of cloth. They can often be seen in the early morning or at dusk, standing silently in small groups, always at the same spot, while studiously ignoring each other.

For all this flim flammery, they are still traditional Gnomes, who are just trying to appear different to their northern cousins.

THE FANCY DRESS GNOME
GNOMUS ANGLIENSIS EROTICUS

As in all human cultures, sex is very important, after all we are talking about the propagation of the species. This is also true with Gnomes, who have a full and active sex life which, luckily for them, lasts for many, many decades.

Gnomes are strictly monogamous, but a marriage that lasts for more than a hundred years has to have a degree of imagination and variety to make it work. Also, because Gnomes do not suffer from headaches, there can be NO excuse!

They tell me they have a full, active and very stimulating love life. To aid this intense love life, the Gnomes have two reference books. The first is the world famous "GNOMASUTRA" and the second, the lesser known volume entitled "GNOMAEROTICA". Both books are a fascinating manual of love making. In fact to work through them you would need the life span of a Gnome.

It would seem that Gnomes have all the sexual preferences and tastes of humans - and more! Hieronymus Goodfellow persuaded his wife Gladiolus to show me her Miss Whippy Gnome outfit. The pink wellies I found very fetching!

THE FOREST GNOMES
GNOMUS ANGLIENSIS SHERWOODII

Deep in the heart of the Great Central, or Middle Forest, often referred to by us humans as Sherwood Forest, there is a clan of Gnomes who are specialist foresters. Whereas Gnomes in general will live in a variety of habitats and are very adaptable, this clan is found only in the forest of Middle Anglia, now currently being greatly expanded with new plantings. The Gnomes here have a collective surname of Sherwood, hence our name for the forest was in fact taken from the Gnome Clan name.

All Gnomes are obliged by tradition and Gnome Law to wear red Hattons. The Gnomes of this vast forest area are the only exception. Their Hattons are green, various shades of green, but always green. The dye is extracted from the plant, Dyers Greenweed.

There is a legend of a bandit who lived in this forest once upon a time called Robin Hood. He was famous for his skills with a longbow. We can find no evidence for this and he probably never existed. But the Sherwood clan of Gnomes do exist and it would appear that the Ancient Britons confused these Gnomes, their green apparel and their SHORT bows, with the bandit Robin of Loxley.

Some Gnomologists maintain the character of mythology called Cupid came from this forest. Legend has it that a pair of lovers were entwined in the bracken deep in the forest when the upper party of the union received an arrow in his exposed buttocks, the arrow having been fired by a Gnome. Affronted by this gross and indecent behaviour in his forest, the Gnome shot the offending party with his Short Bow. This was then seen as Cupid and his bow.

The Forest Gnomes are respected as the experts on all things relating to forests. It is to them that all other Gnomes turn when they require advice and information on nuts, fruit, timber and forest lore.

THE NORTH MOORLAND GNOME
GNOMUS ANGLIENSIS BLUNTICUS

Down the central spine of Anglia (England), there are long ranges of high rounded hills, called Moors. These are bleak, inhospitable, cold exposed places. Humans live in the sheltered valleys below the moors but on the high moors there are Gnomes, especially in the far north of Anglia. These Gnomes are the hardiest of all the Anglian Gnomes, and have become well adapted to the harsh environment. They speak in low gruff voices, unlike the trill of Gnomes to the South. They are reputed to be very blunt and do not suffer fools readily.

These Gnomes are experts on foraging on the high moors. They collect nuts, berries and roots. The Gnome in the illustration is carrying their traditional tools, the nut cracking hammer and a root and bulb extractor. Their homes are usually found in the gnarled roots of ancient, wind bent hawthorn trees.

The northern moors are renowned for their strong, bitterly cold winds, so the Gnomes are usually seen with their hat's earflaps down and their chinstraps securely tied. Without this precaution, their Hattons (hats) blow off.

Your best chance of seeing one of these secretive Northern Gnomes is on a windy day when you might catch a glimpse of a Gnome frantically chasing his errant hat. So famous has this sight been over the millennia that in the English County of Yorkshire there is a famous song called:

"An Ickle Gnome Bar Tat."
(A little Gnome without his hat)

THE NORTH MOORLAND GNOME
GNOMUS ANGLIENSIS BLUNTICUS

CALEDONIAN LOWLAND GNOME
GNOMUS CALEDONIENSIS LOWLANDICUS

Once upon a time, all Gnomes dressed in a plaid skirt, woven with their respective clan colours. It was called a KILTIE. This form of dress was abandoned hundreds of years ago in most Gnome Clans for the simple reason - chilblains. If you ever experience a winter in the north when you have an icy blast howling round and through your exposed nether regions, you too would rapidly cover up. This proves the incredible resilience of these Lowland Gnomes that they still wear the traditional KILTIE.

Of course for the Country of Scotland, this is a huge tourist benefit as every year millions of foreign tourists visit Scotland, just to get a glimpse of the tiny be-kilted Gnomes.

The Lowland Gnomes of Caledonia have become the keepers of one of Gnomedoms most ancient and venerated traditions. In fact it was here that the ancient 'NOSEPIPE' originated in the dawn of time, long before any humans inhabited these Islands. This musical instrument has spread as far as Australia and is probably the most common of the Gnome musical instruments.

There is nothing quite so romantic as the sound of the Nosepipe being skilfully played by a Lowland Gnome amongst the beautiful flowering heather.

CALEDONIAN HIGHLAND GNOME
GNOMUS CALEDONIENSIS HILANDICUS

In the far north of Caledonia, in the land of granite mountains, wind and snow, live arguably the hardiest, toughest and most resilient of all the Gnomes. These are the Caledonian Highland Gnomes, readily identified by their characteristic flame red hair and beards. This characteristic is unique to this Clan of Gnomes.

Gnomelets all have red hair until puberty, when the male Gnomes develop their steel grey hair and beards. Professors Retsof's research has shown that Gnomes have incredibly high levels of testosterone which causes their hair to turn to the characteristic grey-white and thin on top, so that at puberty Gnomes always go bald.

Female Gnomettes start with the same red hair, which on puberty turns to the characteristic straw gold, and remains the same colour for their entire lives.

For some reason, not yet fully understood, the Caledonian Highland Gnomes genetically keep their red hair, which can make them look fierce. Truth to tell, this is entirely false. The harshness of their lives makes them some of the friendliest and least suspicious Gnomes of all.

The Gnome illustrated here is wearing warm TREWLETS in his clan colours. He carries what looks suspiciously like a hot water bottle but is, in fact, a flexible and unbreakable flask of single malt, carried for strictly medicinal purposes. On his belt he carries a foraging hatchet and a pointed knife for holding onto, and climbing, ice sheets, called a GIRK. The ear flaps on their Hattons are worn down, even in summer. Note also the fur boots and jerkin for added warmth.

CALEDONIAN HIGHLAND GNOME
GNOMUS CALEDONIENSIS HILANDICUS

THE CAMBRIAN MOUNTAIN GNOME
GNOMUS CAMBRIENSIS SNOWDONICUS

In the North of Cambria (Wales) there is a mighty mountain range, not as large as the Caledon Mountains, but still large enough to support its own Clan of specialist Gnomes, the Cambrian Mountain Gnomes. These Gnomes have become highly specialised to living on the numerous cliffs and sheer rock faces of the mountains. The best places to see them are on the warmer south facing faces.

These diminutive Mountain specialists are consummate mountaineers. They move across sheer smooth rock faces with the agility of little mountain goats - well most of the time. They have absolutely no fear of heights and take the most extraordinary risks as they move around their mountain home.

They speak the same universal language of GNO, but their accent is so strong that they and the southern Clans do not understand each other. They are some of the most enthusiastic singers of all Gnome Clans, one of their most famous anthems being

"Gnomes of Harlech."

These Mountain Clans, because of the sparseness and harshness of their habitat, do not like other Clans moving into their territory. So this is an area where you will frequency see the threat display, the GNAKA. And it is probably the best place to see the ritualised combat, GUDO.

THE *WEST CAMBRIAN GNOME*
GNOMUS CAMBRIENSIS HUMIDICUS

On the western side of the land of Cambria and even more so to the west of the island of Hibernia, the land is subject to the constant onslaught of the deep weather depressions that crash in from the Atlantic Ocean. These deep depressions bring high, dangerous winds, especially when you are of diminutive stature, and huge amounts of horizontal, driving rain.

The consequence of living with this weather means the Gnomes of the region walk with a hunched over gait, commonly known as the "Western Stoop". Even in the extremely rare event of a fine day, they still walk bent over as if they are being battered and soaked.

Along the west of Cambria, one of the great Gnomish delicacies is seaweed which is harvested at low tide and made into a rather delicious cake called GNAVA Bread.

Right down in the South of Cambria, there are specialist Gnome Clans who tunnel into the hillsides in search of the metals used by the highly skilled Forge Master Gnomes.

The Gnome on the opposite page heard about umbrellas from the Southern Commuter Gnomes but, as you can see, umbrellas are of little or no use in the west.

Across the wild water from the shores of Cambria, there is the Island of Hibernia. The Gnomes of Hibernia are distinctive Clans under their own Grand Council. There are legends on that Island of Little People, but these appear to be different from the distinctive Gnome population.

Hibernia is a land of rivers because, as with Cambria, it takes the full force of the mighty depressions rolling in off the Atlantic. Thus the Hibernian Gnomes are virtually identical to the Cambrian Gnomes. Indeed, the Gnomes in Hibernia always say that the Cambrian Gnomes are in reality the Hibernian Gnomes who could not swim.

The specialist water transport of both these Gnome populations is the small round boat, the GORACLE. The Goracle is a small circular boat that comfortably carries one Gnome who has one paddle. The direction of travel, because of the boat's shape, is frequently in ever decreasing circles.

Small animals frequently hitch a ride across rivers and streams, but the Gnomes biggest fear is playful otters who love to make the boat spin on the water, resulting in very green, seasick Gnomes.

The Goracle is made of a lattice frame of hazel and willow sticks woven together and covered with patches of fabric treated with water-proof tree resin. Sometimes small animal skins are used, but as the Gnomes use nearly all the available skins for clothing and boots, the hides are in short supply, so the majority of Goracles are covered in treated woven fabric.

Once again, I must stress that Gnomes do not kill small animals, their hides are taken from animals that have died naturally. They use the bark of the Goat Willow as tannin to cure the hides.

THE BADLANDS YOBBOGNOME
GNOMUS HORRIBILIS

In the marginal regions where no one goes, called the 'Badlands', there are a few, in fact very few, outcast Gnomes called the YOBBOGNOMES. These are Gnomes who have, to be quite frank, completely lost the plot. They are outcasts, feared and dreaded by all other Gnomes.

Their appearance is totally different from normal Gnomes. They wear an almost black Hatton, a Jerkin to match, numerous brass rings through their ears and noses and their skin is tattooed using Woad. Their beards are grizzled, short and heavily stained.

Professor Retsof has made a detailed study of these antisocial Yobbognomes and has concluded that they are genetic aberrations. They are incapable of any form of social inter-action, and their vocabulary has been reduced over the years to simply snarling the same expression over and over again;

"WOT-YEW-LOOKINAT", "WOT-YEW-LOOKINAT."

This is invariably followed by an assault with sticks, stones, pebbles or anything else that comes to hand. These Gnomes favour evil tempered 'PIT-WEASELS' as pets and companions. These fighting weasels have docked tails making them even more aggressive.

These Gnomes are rare and should not concern the dedicated Gnomologist, but be sure, in the rare event of seeing one, to avoid him at all costs.

THE BADLANDS YOBBOGNOME
GNOMUS HORRIBILIS

131

Gnomes sketched near
New York

Beautifully crafted
sheath knife.

THE GNOMES OF NORTH AMERICA OR NEW GNOMELAND

THE NORTHERN MIGRATORY GNOME
GNOMUS MIGRATIENS

The original Gnomes in North America, or as the Gnomes prefer to call it, New Gnomeland, arrived via the Islands of Fire and Ice in the North of the great ocean we call the Atlantic. They came and settled the continent before any humans and now they are as numerous across the continent as they are across the European Continent.

The Gnomes spread along the waterways, travelling all across the continent using small birch bark boats called Ganoes, which hundreds of years later were copied by the early human inhabitants. There is some speculation that Gnomes arrived in America on the Mayflower as tiny stowaways, but ancient archaeological evidence shows they were more than likely the first inhabitants of the continent.

There are several pioneering Clans of Gnomes who still travel constantly along the thousands of miles of waterways across the continent.

Like bears, Gnomes tend to spend the severe continental winters in a state of semi-hibernation, coming out to feed and take the air when the occasional warm front crosses the continent. Because their ancestors were brave enough to cross the Atlantic in their dugout boats, or fly over on the backs of migrating birds, their descendants are some of the most rugged, and certainly the most adventurous, Gnomes of all.

This Gnome has his belongings in a plaid hold all, which was much copied and called a carpetbag.

GNOMES AND BEARS

On our many research field trips to North America we have discovered that the bears, both Black and Grizzly, have a unique relationship with Gnomes. To be exact, they love each other.

Bears are totally fascinated with Gnomes. Originally when Gnomes were first fanning out over the entire continent, they were in great fear and trepidation of the massive bears they encountered.

Coming face to face with a Grizzly as a human is a very moving experience, their size and sheer power totally overwhelming. Imagine then, meeting a bear for the first time when you are the size of a little Gnome.

However bears are extremely fond of Gnomes, as are all the other wild animals and birds found on the continent. The wildlife and Gnomes live together in perfect harmony. There is quite a lot of evidence that Gnomes will give a warning call when there are hunters in the area, that is always heeded by the animals. The call is an undulating whistle that is too high a pitch for humans to hear but animals, with their superior hearing, hear very clearly over great distances.

Gnomes, the world over, find the human desire to hunt animals for fun totally incomprehensible. Yet they do not have a problem with predators taking animals as food. Strangely there are no records of predators taking Gnomes in North America, despite there being several large predators that could.

GNOMES AND BEARS

One of the most endearing facts about the North American Gnomes is the closeness of their relationship with bears.

Gnomes have probably been on the continent for several thousand years so this Bear/Gnome relationship has very deep and long established roots. There is anecdotal evidence that they have the same deep relationship with Polar Bears, but I must admit this is one aspect we have not researched. I believe the Institute of Gnomology is currently organising an expedition to the north of Norway to research this subject.

This relationship is so close that mother bears let their cubs carry Gnomes around with them for comfort. Incredibly the Gnomes do not seem evenly remotely worried by this treatment. In fact, I would go so far as to say that they positively enjoy the relationship.

These Gnomes are known as 'TEDDY-GNOMES'.
The Gnomes stay with the bear cubs for their first
summer, and in return get the pick of the
fruits and berries the bears find.

THE ROCKY MOUNTAIN GNOME
GNOMUS FRIDGIDICUS

The mighty Rocky Mountains, that huge range of high mountains which run down the centre of North America like a massive spine, dividing the continent, has its own unique Clan of Mountain Gnomes. These are Gnomes who specialise in high altitude living.   Examination by Professor Retsof has revealed that these Gnomes have inordinately large lungs and an exceptionally high red blood cell count. They are superbly adapted to the high altitude mountain life.

They wear specialised clothing. Their Hats, or Hattons are made in the only North American Hat making centre, at a place called 'MEDICINE HAT' in Alberta, Canada. All North American Gnome Hats or Hattons are made there. The French Canadian Gnomes wear, of course, the Bonnet Rouge.

The Rocky Gnome Hatton is made from incredibly warm squirrel fur and comes down so low that it covers their ears.   It is also stiffened with fine willow wands so that the snow slides off it. Their clothing is of the thickest woollen weave, and their jerkin is of thick waterproof fur. The Gnomes always carry a backpack containing emergency rations of dried fruit and nuts. They also carry a sleeping bag that is made of fine down for the cold nights.

They either travel on skis or snowshoes. There have been persistent rumours of a North American Yeti, or ape man of the mountains.   Our research shows that this is in fact the Rocky Mountain Gnome or "LITTLE FOOT".

THE ROCKY MOUNTAIN GNOME
GNOMUS FRIDGIDICUS

THE DESERT GNOME
GNOMUS DESSICATUS

There are several deserts in North America. These are harsh dry lands freezing cold at night and searing hot by day; areas with their own unique wildlife inhabitants.

Several Gnome Clans inhabit these deserts. Like the Mountain Gnomes, they are highly specialised and well able to cope with the harsh conditions. One of their notable features is their ability to lick their wrists in the hottest time of the day. The moisture then evaporates and cools the Gnome's blood. The only other example we have found of this behaviour is the Australian Bush Gnome.

These Gnomes, often called GERONIGNOMES, are experts at living off the seemingly barren land and they never need to find water as they extract all the moisture they need from desert succulents or cacti. These are the Gnomes who invented the fine suede jacket with fringed sleeves, so much copied by the later human backwoodsmen like Davy Crockett. The Gnomes always carry a backpack with essentials for survival, including water bottles that have been filled with cactus juice. They often sing as they walk, a favourite song being

"Gnome, Gnome on the range."

Geronignomes always carry the forked snake stick because the desert is full of amorous rattle snakes who, like all other snakes, love Gnomes. Just like other snakes, their breath is terrible, but fortunately they wag their tales in pleasure at seeing Gnomes, which forewarns the Gnomes, thus giving them time to fend off the snake's amorous advances.

Desert Gnomes are usually to be found living in small nomadic groups.

THE DESERT GNOME
GNOMUS DESSICATUS

Chasing a Bumble bee.

Gnomes sketched
in the valleys of
NewSouth Wales

Gnomette, hair style
indicates
married status.

Small shovel for
excavating Fogou.

THE GNOMES OF AUSTRALIA

THE AUSTRALIAN BUSH GNOME
GNOMUS OUTBACKUS

Gnomologists in Australia have long speculated about the possibility of there being a clan of specialised Bush Gnomes, or 'DINKUMS' who live in the harsh desert like interior or the outback.

A few years back we embarked on a six month expedition to see if we could find the legendary 'Dinkum' or Bush Gnome. After months of searching we were, quite frankly, at the point of giving up. We were camped about three hundred miles from Alice Springs when, quite by chance, we literally stumbled on a small Clan of Dinkums. Now, much to our relief, we could say that the legendary Australian Bush Gnome actually existed.

These are classic Gnomes with some subtle differences; the Gnomes wear long shorts for coolness, exposing their red knees. Their boots are tightly strapped on and they wear a jerkin without an undershirt. On their arms and Hatton, they wear embroidered bands with the triangular Gnome Hat symbol. On their belts they have the traditional pouch, plus a pair of water bottles and, what is for Gnomes, a really large knife. They have a line of Macadamia Nuts hanging from the brim of their hats to keep the ever present flies out of their eyes.

The Dinkum carry traditional 'GNOMERANGS' for knocking Macadamia nuts out of the trees. This is like a Boomerang but the 'bend' is in the opposite direction.

We found that these Dinkums were the friendliest Gnomes we had ever encountered. They were totally relaxed in our presence, and made us very welcome.

THE AUSTRALIAN BUSH GNOME
GNOMUS OUTBACKUS

THE AUSTRALIAN BUSH GNOME
GNOMUS OUTBACKUS

One of the most extraordinary discoveries we made about the Dinkum is their choice of musical instrument - The NOSE PIPE, or what they call the 'WIDGIWOO', after the strange haunting sound it makes. The instrument is exactly the same instrument that we find on the British Isles. The pipe is made from a wood the Gnomes call 'NOSEPIPEWOOD', a low growing tree that has hollow stems.

The Nosepipe, like everything else down under, is decorated with the Hatton Chevron design. Only certain Gnomes are musicians, and we were treated to a recital by a lone Gnome we found some twenty miles from our camp. The Dinkum played for hours, performing an intricate dance routine to accompany his playing, the Macadamia fly screen waving about and above his Hatton, as he jumped and pranced.

As you can see from the illustration, he carries, relative to his size, an extremely large sheath knife, used for digging up the succulent roots and tubers that make up the bulk of the Dinkum's diet.

Professor Retsof's research into the genes of these Gnomes, plus archaeological evidence we unearthed in the Bungle Bungles, show that these are a very unique species of Gnomes, who have been on the continent far longer than any humans.

There are other Australian Gnomes, but many of these were introduced with the early settlers, and are very much Gnomes of urban areas and farming areas.

THE AUSTRALIAN BUSH GNOME
GNOMUS OUTBACKUS

THE AUSTRALIAN BUSH GNOME
GNOMUS OUTBACKUS

Like the bears in North America, the kangaroos and wallabies have developed a strong bond with the Gnomes, the Dinkum in particular.   The kangaroos allow the Gnomes to travel in their pouch. This means Gnomes can effortlessly travel great distances.

Kangaroos have long known that a Joey in the pouch is far better behaved when accompanied by a Gnome or two. The young roos will play for hours with the ever patient Gnomes. The Gnomes, on the other hand, seem to get a real thrill when travelling in huge leaps and bounds in the kangaroo's pouch.

Australia has a worldwide reputation for having some of the most toxic snakes and spiders in the world. This does not affect the Gnomes, who are immune to all types of venom. As with snakes in other parts of the world, the Australian snakes are over fond of Gnomes, causing much embarrassment to the Gnomes.

There is anecdotal evidence of predation on Gnomes in Queensland by the giant cane toads. These huge amphibians are reputed to swallow Gnomelets whole. So far this has yet to be proved.

That other Australian super predator, the Salt Water Crocodile, seems to avoid Gnomes, almost as if it was in fear of them. Scientists have a theory that the crocodiles see the Red Hatton, worn by the Gnomes, as a warning sign and avoid them. Once again much like the Masai's red shuka and lions.

THE AUSTRALIAN BUSH GNOME
GNOMUS OUTBACKUS

SOME LITTLE KNOWN FACTS ABOUT GNOMES

THE CHURCH STEEPLE

In the dawn of time on the fair Isle of Britannia there came a wandering Holy Man who answered to the name of CLEARVOICE MYRTLEBERGER.

He travelled the Islands visiting the Ancient Britons in their rude hovels, preaching his Divine message of Fire, Brimstone, Torment, Virgins and similar. So successful was his fiery oratory, that wherever he went, he started to draw large crowds. The weather in Britannia was then, as it is now; cold, wet, damp and drear, causing the Britons to huddle in their hovels, refusing to even visit the local mall.

Myrtleberger decided that he needed a large, easy to find enclosed space where he could preach his message in relative comfort. A very, very large hut was the obvious answer.

One day while visiting some hovels in the hills, he noticed that the Village Chief lived in a rather natty, stone built hovel. This was the ideal solution; purpose built, solid stone meeting houses.

But how to get his huge stone buildings noticed? That was the problem.

Late one evening, while crossing the Pennine Hills, he looked up and saw a high ridge that was lined with a series of large boulders. It was here that he decided to camp for the night, in the shelter of the huge boulders. As he sat facing the sunset, meditating, he became aware that he was not alone.

There in front of him, silhouetted against the setting sun, contemplating the day's end, was a little Gnome.

Myrtleberger stared at the silhouette and bellowed "EUREKA!" (or something similar), frightening the daylights out of the Gnome, who fled.

Myrtleberger had realised that if he built a building with a tall tower capped off with a Gnome Hat, it would be visible for miles!

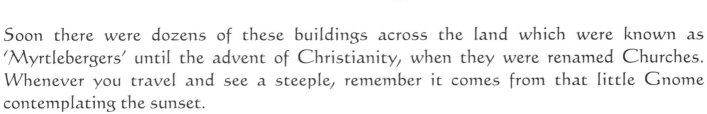

Soon there were dozens of these buildings across the land which were known as 'Myrtlebergers' until the advent of Christianity, when they were renamed Churches. Whenever you travel and see a steeple, remember it comes from that little Gnome contemplating the sunset.

THE BOBBY

Sir Robert Peel, Father of modern policing, spent virtually all of his free time Gnome watching. One of his favourite haunts was St James's Park in London, where there was a large and very successful Gnome Clan. Gnomology is a hobby that requires great dedication as Gnomes are best seen at dawn or sunset. So it was on one misty dawn morning, when London still slept, that Sir Robert came upon a small Gnome telling off a badly behaved duck. So impressed was Sir Robert with the Gnomes authority, and the way the chastened duck stopped misbehaving, that he came up with the idea of dressing a body of men in Gnome hats as peacekeepers.

THE BOBBY

On the way home from St. James's Park, Sir Robert passed the Palace just in time to see the Changing of the Guard. This, combined with his idea of men in Gnome hats, gave him the idea to get the men into uniform with a pointed Gnome Hat. This is how the first 'Bobby-Gnomes' came to be. These men were hugely successful and crime ceased to be a problem. The dye for the uniforms was extracted from the Gnome dye plant called WOAD. This dye was used right up till the 1930's.

The Gnome hat was later reinforced and badges added. So when you see a Bobby on the Beat, remember his inspiration came from a Gnome.

THE THREE WISE GNOMES

SEE NO EVIL, HEAR NO EVIL, SPEAK NO EVIL

LORD KITCHENER

General Kitchener spent all his free time in the countryside Gnome watching (he was a Gnomologist of international repute).

At the start of the First World War, the Government wanted a design for an Army recruitment poster. Kitchener came up with a Gnome design. This was rejected by the Government who substituted the gnome with a picture of Kitchener himself.

Kitchener never got over the rejection of his design, so for the first time ever, here is the original design.

YOUR GNOME NEEDS

YOU

THE DUNCE

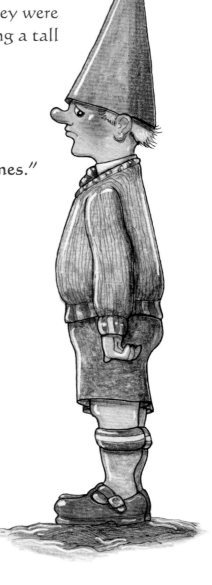

Starting in the 1790's, schoolteachers used a cruel and humbling punishment for children, in that, when their schoolwork was wrong, or they misbehaved, they were made to stand in the corner of the class wearing a tall conical hat and were referred to as a 'Dunce'.

Fortunately, when Britain joined the European Union this practise was banned as being:

"Demeaning, Insulting and Injurious to Gnomes."

Quite right too!

And finally.....

Nelson's last words to Captain Hardy were not **"Kiss me Hardy"**. They were, according to Hardy's secret diary;

"Look after my Gnomes, Hardy".

ANGLIA: The Country we know as ENGLAND

AUGER SHELL: Spiral sea shell which is used by gnomes as musical instrument, rather like a bugle.

BAABERRY: Soft fruit we call Bilberry.

BITTERBERRY: Soft fruit we call Cranberry.

BLACK GNOMBREAD : Rye bread.

BLUEPOUND: Rock from ancient volcano crater used for pestle and mortar.

BRITANNIA: The island of Britain.

BUSH BABY: Small African primate closely related to Gnomes.

CALEDONIA : The country we know as Scotland.

CAMBRIA: The country we know as Wales.

COBMATS: The nuts we call hazel nuts.

DINKUM: The Australian Bush Gnome.

DOLGNOMEN: Three standing stones with capping stone.

FOGOU: The Gnome's underground home.

FROZENLAND: The country of Greenland.

GANOE: Small boat used by Gnomes.

GERONIGNOMES: American desert Gnomes.

G-GNOME: Gnomes genetic code.

GIRK: Small pointed dagger for ice climbing.

GOLLENTA: Porridge like dish made from milled Sweet Chestnut.

GORACLE: Circular boat that is almost uncontrollable.

GNAKA: Gnome threat display used in territorial disputes

GNAVA BREAD: Seaweed dish from Cambria.

GNO: The language of Gnomes. (i.e. Gnomes - the people of GNO)
GNOMA SUTRA: The Erotic book of Gnomes.
GNOMA EROTICA: Volume Two.
GNOMEHENGE: Circle of standing stones.
GNOMEKINS: Baby Gnomes.
GNOMELETS: Teenage or Sub-Adult Gnomes.
GNOMENHIR: Standing stone.
GNOMERANG: Like a Boomerang but goes the other way.
GNOMETORS: Balancing rocks.
GNOMETTE: Female Gnome.
GUDO: The Gnome Martial Art.
HATTON: The Red Hat worn by Gnomes, also called the Bonnet Rouge.
HIBERNIA:The land we humans call Ireland.
ISLAND OF FIRE: The country we call Iceland.
KORNMAT: Acorns.
KILTIE: Skirt like garment worn by Lowland Gnomes in Caledonia.
LITTLE FOOT: The Rocky Mountain Gnome.
MOOBERRY: Cowberry.
NEW GNOMELAND: North America.
NOSEPIPE: Musical instrument made from Elder wood.
PARADISE BERRY: Strawberry.
PILGNOMAGE: Pilgrimage.
PITWEASEL: Obnoxious weasel kept as pets by YOBBOGNOMES.

PORTERGNOMES: Gnomes that carry goods from Clan to Clan.
POUNDING STONE: Pestle and Mortar for Nuts and Seeds.
PRICKLEBERRY: Blackberry.
SHERPAGNOMES: Another name for Portergnomes.
SOUTERRAINS: Underground dwellings used by Gnomes.
SUNBERRY: Cloudberry.
SWEETBERRY: Raspberry.
TEDDY-GNOMES: Comforters for Bear Cubs.
TREWLETS: Woollen trousers worn by Caledonian Highland Gnomes.
TRILIGNOMES: Standing stones in groups of three.
TURNCONE: High tech. hat (HATTON) making machine.
WEEM: Another name for Gnome underground dwelling.
WINEBERRY: Elderberry.
WIDGIWOO: Outback Gnome name for the NOSEPIPE.
WOGGLETOG: The intricate piece of machinery used in HATTON making.
YOBBOGNOME: Name of uncouth, antisocial and all round nasty Clan
of noxious Gnomes, avoided by all normal Gnomes.

The International Institute of Gnomology

Be it known to all Men and Gnomes that
Armand Foster
has this first day of April in the
year nineteen eighty five
been made by gracious consent
of the Grand Council
of the Gnomes
a fellow of
the International Institute
of
Gnomology
for his research and
efforts to promote
the rights and well being
of
GNOMES

Given under my hand at
München Gnomebach

D Retsof

Herr Professor Doktor Retsof
Director of the Institute

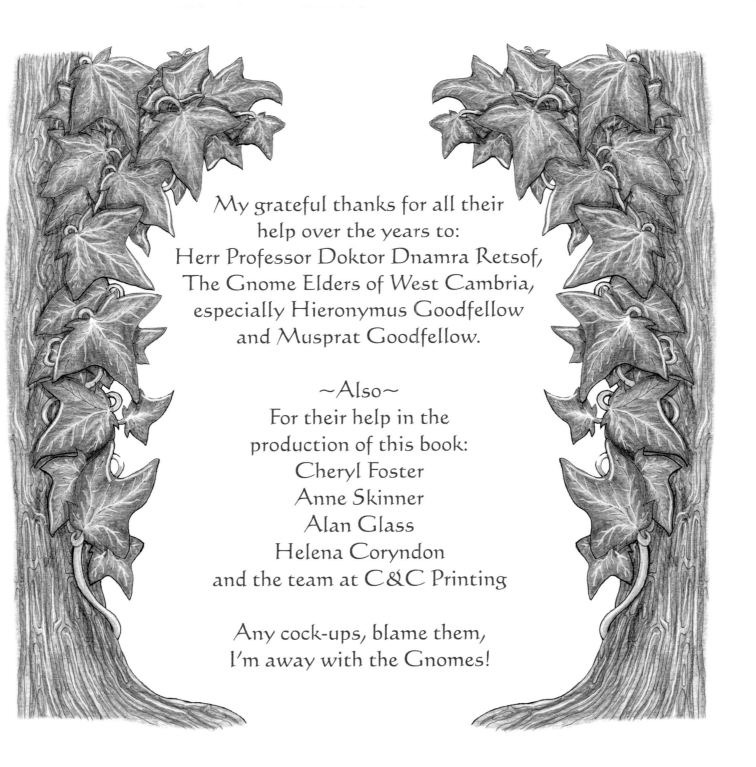

My grateful thanks for all their
help over the years to:
Herr Professor Doktor Dnamra Retsof,
The Gnome Elders of West Cambria,
especially Hieronymus Goodfellow
and Musprat Goodfellow.

~Also~
For their help in the
production of this book:
Cheryl Foster
Anne Skinner
Alan Glass
Helena Coryndon
and the team at C&C Printing

Any cock-ups, blame them,
I'm away with the Gnomes!